The
Far
Corner
Of
The
Garden

The Far Corner Of The Garden

Geri Harding

Library of Congress Cataloging-in-Publication Data

Harding, Geri.
    The far corner of the garden / Geri Harding.
        p.   cm.
    ISBN 1-882892-03-8 : $19.25
    1. Painting, American.   2. Artists, Mentally handicapped--United
States.   3. Artists, Physically handicapped--United States.
    I. Title.
ND205.H27   1993
759.13'087--dc20   93-6998
                                                               CIP

Creative Energies
Publishers
P.O.Box 1418
Roosevelt,Utah   84066
Tel#(801)353-4125
Tel#(801)722-3604
Printed in Mexico

This Book is Dedicated to

the beloved artists
whose work
this is.

FORWARD FOR GERI'S BOOK

When I first saw these art works some years ago, I was overcome by the honest and profound simplicity of expression. That very quality that such modern Masters as Picasso, Klee and Miro tried to recapture is evident here in every passage of color, shape and line. The intuitive quality of innocence is a rare and precious gift, which most of us lose in the complexities of our lives. If we could but briefly return to the spontaneity of pure expression, such joy would we find!

It is man's inherent nature to create, to express himself, to say "I am". This is not a hobby, nor a frill; it is a necessity. Our creativity is expressed in a variety of ways, but it must be expressed or we lose our individuality, our identity.

It is Geri's remarkable gift to see that treasure in overlooked and unlikely places, and to share that intimate knowledge with us. Geri is eminently qualified as artist, writer, teacher, wife, mother, grandmother — to see and feel deeply, to encourage and nourish, to guide and to let go - that creative spirit which dwells within us all.

Christy King

Who is Christy King?

In addition to being one of the most accomplished artists in the state of Utah, Christy King is:

High School Art Teacher
Adjunct Faculty-Utah State University

Member:

     Utah Art Education Association
     National Art Education Association
     Associated Utah Artists
     Utah Watercolor Society
     American Association of University Women
     Board of Directors, Utah Humanities Council

AN INTRODUCTION BY THE AUTHOR

The art work in this book expresses the Universal Soul in the language of forms, colors and space; the very language that shakes us out of the ruts of ordinary perception.
Most of the work was done by small twisted fingers and damaged brains. It is my hope that the viewer will look beyond the physical infirmities of these paintings and see the beauty in honest expression.
This collection is the result of my many years as an art teacher to handicapped people. Because of my closeness to them I took it upon myself to give each piece of art a few words of interpretation. The viewer may very well see a different image and give a new interpretation; and that is as it should be.
Enjoy!

Geri Harding

The
Far
Corner
Of
The
Garden

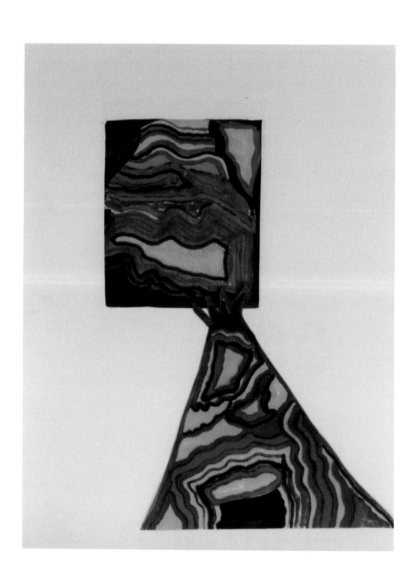

Tee Pees have all Disappeared on the Reservations.
You have to make Your own Reservations to Have a Tee Pee Now.

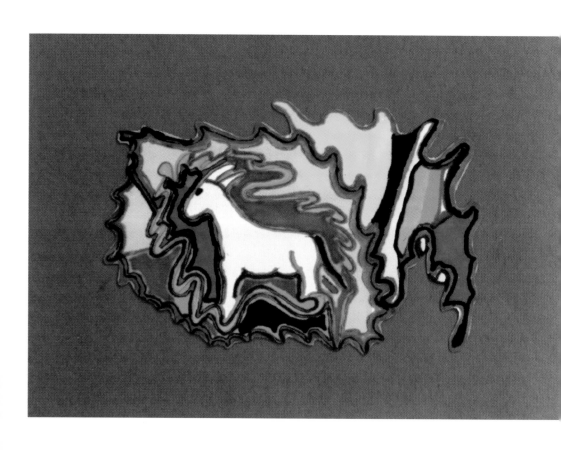

I live in a
Country
That loves animals.
It's a good thing
For I am a horse.

A rare beauty
Is the beauty of dog.
He eats from
Silver dish,
And plays with
Yellow ball.
He comes when I
Call
So I can beat him.

A ridem' ropem'
Cowboy passed in
The night
And left me
One golden boot.
He wanted to stay
But he had to go.
Good bye.

Crazy old
Roadrunner
Makes me laugh.
He's not really
Real, you know.
Really real things
Aren't very funny.
I like the roadrunner
Show.

Each day I find
Another gift,
Out by the side
Of the house.
I put it in my
Private place
To be examined
At a later
Date.

I   don't know why
The flowers die
When winter comes.
Most of all
I don't know why
We paint them in
Their
Coffins.

The wind blows down
Across the field
And swirls the
Lifeless leaves around.
I run to catch
These
That the winter
Kills
And bury them
Safely
In the ground.

My heart is broken
Some today.
Head aches...
Stomach whirls...
Colors gray.
Everything is upside
Down.
Lines lean and sway.
Just don't feel good
Today.

I made the Titanic!
I broke the Titanic!
I am God!
What say ye?

Julie Lavine wants me on TV.
I wonder what she wants of me?
I think I'll make her a bird
You see.....cause only
God
Can make a tree.

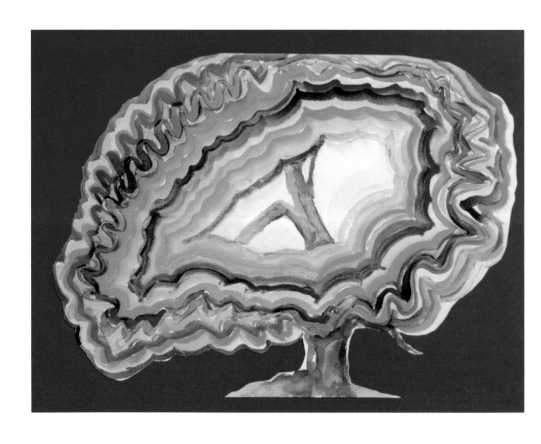

Johnny Cash owns
The greatest tree
In the world.
It is red and pink
And green and
And.....
Gold.

Someday, we say
We'll move away
To that tall house
On the hill.
We'll have a red
Roof.....and a
Carpet to match.
Some puppies and
Goats..... and
Some eggs to hatch.
Then pretend we
Have a friend
Who'll come our
Way
Someday
We say.

We'll plant window
Flowers in the house
On the hill.
They'll hang from the
Ceiling and grow up
From the sill.
And all the people
Passing by
Will look up and say
My My.

The red candle cries;
Tears leave heavy
Streaks
Downward. She
Grows shorter and
Fatter.... until
Finally...
Santa Claus
Comes.

God made neighbors.
Man made the
Neighborhood.
And all this I saw
From where I stood.

You are good
For the garden,
Straight and
Pretty.
I wonder why
You stretch down
And touch me.
I love you.

In all the world
I only know one
Thing for sure:
Hunger is the
Very worst
Disease
Ever
Invented.

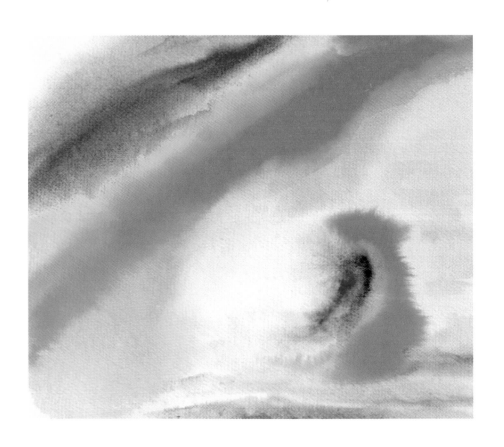

The fiery rainbow drops
To kiss the water.
The waves leap in
Playfull glee.
Who am I, that
These startling
Wonders
I see.

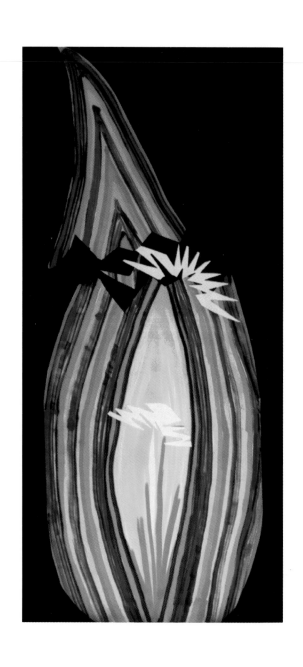

Who would ever
Believe it?
How can something
So
Eternal .....
Break?

I see me on
A higher hill
Looking up...
And down below
There I am...
Watching.

I'm not afraid
Of things;
Even the
Crisscrossings
In the sky.
No one knows it...but
If you ride the beams
You can safely...fly.

The face comes
From an earlier
Beauty,
Too far and faint
To share.
The face leans
Down to kiss me
And leaves white
Tears in the
Scraggles of
My hair.

A great and handsome
Hero
Stood tall - up to the
Sky!
People came to watch
Him lift his trumpet
High....
Then slowly they
Began to see
That
The great and handsome
Hero
Was
Only me.

I live in
The far corner
Of the
Garden.
Thank you for
Allowing me to
Stay.
I didn't mean
To make the
Garden
Ugly.

From the window
I see it all:
The Spring,
The Summer,
The Fall.
I hear the water
Splash and play
And then....
We all
Go away.

I wish I could help
All the people
That die
On the six o'clock
News
Before they are carried
Into heaven
On wings of
Thunder.

Alone at dinner time
Is not so dumb.
I bow my head and
Say a prayer.
Behold....
God
Has come.

I pledge allegiance
To the flag
Before the
Thunder comes
To carry it to
Heaven.

I wondered today
How it could be
That the large and
Lovely
Soul
Dwells within the
Small
And wretched
Me.

I don't know why
It's dull and
Drab,
With no golden
Leaves to shine.
I only know
For sure
This tree is
Mine.

And a great star sent
Down its light
That warm and dark
Summer night;
A baby was born.
No wise men came
No presents,
No songs of blessed
Joy...But
God
Looked down and
Winked.
He
Knew his boy.

Alone I make my
Little path;
Alone I stand and
Fall.
Perhaps then
The lesson is:
Disattachment
True love
After all.